Thank you for a woolly jumper

Patricia & Victor Smeltzer

A LION BOOK

Tring · Batavia · Sydney

Adam had a new woolly jumper
to keep him warm in winter.

"Thank you, **Granny,**
for my jumper,"
said Adam.

"Don't thank me,"
said Granny.
"I only knitted the jumper.
You must thank the one
who sold me the wool."

So Adam went to say
"Thank you" to…

...the **shopkeeper.**

"Thank you, **shopkeeper,**
for the wool for my jumper,"
said Adam.

"Don't thank me,"
said the shopkeeper.
"I only sold the wool.
You must thank the one
who brought the wool to
my shop."

So Adam went to say
"Thank you" to...

...the **delivery man.**

"Thank you, **delivery man,**
for the wool for my jumper,"
said Adam.

"Don't thank me,"
said the man.
"I only took the wool
to the shop.
"You must thank the ones
who gave me the wool."

So Adam went to say
"Thank you" to...

...the **woollen mill workers.**

"Thank you, **mill workers,**
for the wool for my jumper,"
said Adam.

"Don't thank us,"
said the workers.
"We only cleaned, dyed and
spun the raw wool.
You must thank the one
who gave us the wool!"

So Adam went to say
"Thank you" to...

...the **sheep farmer.**

"Thank you, **farmer,**
 for the wool for my jumper,"
 said Adam.

"Don't thank me,"
 said the farmer.
"I only look after my sheep.
 They give the wool.
 I shear it off when it is
 thick and heavy.
 You must thank the sheep
 for giving their woolly coats."

So Adam went to say
"Thank you" to...

...the **sheep.**

"Thank you, **sheep,**
for the wool for my jumper,"
said Adam.

"Don't thank us,"
said the sheep.

"We needed our food
to help us grow our
woolly coats."

So Adam went to say
"Thank you" to...

...the **grass.**

"Thank you, **grass,**
    for the wool for my jumper,"
    said Adam.

"Don't thank me,"
    said the grass.
"I needed other things
    to help me grow.
    You must thank them."

So Adam went to say
"Thank you" to...

...the **soil,**

...rain,

...and **sun.**

"Thank you,
soil, rain and **sun,**
for the wool for my jumper,"
said Adam.

"Don't thank us,"
they all said.
"You must thank the one
who made us."

So Adam said "Thank you" to...

...God.

Adam said this prayer:

"Thank you, **God,**
for making
the **soil, rain** and **sun;**

and for the **grass**
that grows;

Thank you, **God,**
for the **sheep;**

and for the **farmer,**

and for the
mill workers,

and for the
delivery man,

and for the
shopkeeper;

Thank you, **God,**
for my **Granny;**

Thank you, **God,**
for my woolly jumper.
Amen."